KAY THOMPSON'S
MISS POOKY PECKINPAUGH

AND HER SECRET PRIVATE
BOYFRIENDS COMPLETE
WITH TELEPHONE NUMBERS

DRAWINGS BY JOE EULA

HARPER & ROW, PUBLISHERS · NEW YORK, EVANSTON, AND LONDON

FIRST EDITION

LIBRARY OF CONGRESS CATALOG CARD NUMBER: 74-121803

I
Miss
Pooky
Peckinpaugh
am
interested
in
boys
if
they
don't
notice
me
I
find
out
their
telephone
numbers
and
call
them
up
and
if
they
won't
come
to
the
telephone
I
hang
up
and
make
a
notation
in
this
my
secret
private
boyfriends
book

ARTHUR is awful
I mean he acts like an APE...
and about
ARTHUR
at the ANNUAL APRIL ART AUCTION at ARIEL ARTHWEIN'S...?
IT was awful...I mean all this arty art crowd was there
in the ARTHWEIN art alcove...among all those arbutus...
including ARTHUR's antique astrological aunt whom ARTHUR abhors
AND when AUGUST ARTHWEIN...ARIEL's ancient ancestor...opened the
AUCTION with...Good afternoon...Anyone for ARP?...there was
this appalling annoyance coming from the arbor...out where
the awning hangs over the arch...and at first...AUGUST ARTHWEIN
assumed it was ARIEL's Afghan...ANGELICA...who had just arrived
from ARIZONA...and was amused...BUT...IT was ARTHUR...
yelling ARP ARP ARP ARP ARP...and everyone was aghast...A N D
ARTHUR attacked AUGUST ARTHWEIN in this awful animal abandon
in the ankles...with this awful auburn hair...like an animal...
and these APEY arms...IT was AWFUL...and everyone applauded...
and ARTHUR absconded with the ARP...in his ALFA ROMEO...
AAARROOOM and AAAWWWAAAY...IT WAS AWFUL...
Anyway
AUGUST ARTHWEIN is an ass
ARTHUR'S Aunt is an ass
and
ARTHUR is an ass
ALSO
ARTHUR's an AQUARIUS and he's in analysis...AND
I'm awfully afraid he's all animal

Oh ARTHUR
Where ARE You?

ARTHUR AMBROSE AMHERST
203 407...6437
        THAT
AWFUL ANSWERING SERVICE
ALWAYS ANSWERS

BABU is a bore
and
bores me beyond belief...I mean
BABU on the beach...bodysurfing and all bronzed...
with those bleached bangs blowing...in the
blue bandana breeze...is boring...You know?
and
BABU riding bareback on that black horse...
barefoot...barebreasted...
bellbottoms bonging...and bellowing like a
bullfrog...AND belching through the breakers...
I mean it's beautiful...but it's all bones and beerbelly...
You know?
It's so boring...
AND
with BUFFY BLOOMINGDALE...(BAZAAR BEACH ISSUE)...on the back
in THAT bikini with THAT bosom and THAT beauty spot...
It's sooo boring I could burst it's sooo boring...
Besides...
BABU's eyes are too blue...
AND he bores me beyond belief

Oh BABU
You're BLISS
BEAUTIFUL BLUE EYED
B L I S S

BABU BOYNATOVSKY
213 508...5928
THAT
BLASTED TOO BITTER TO BEAR
BUSY BUSY BUZZ

CHAR CHAR is a creep
and he is sooo conceited and sooo condescending I could
choke he's sooo conceited and sooo condescending...AND
with all of that confidence...The creep
Holding court on the curb in front of the CORONET...on that
cream COMANCHE cycle...CAROOOM...clowning like some clod
for his close and copious chums...Completely cracked up...
with his chest caved in and clutching those crutches...
and his collar bone and calves in those clumsy casts...
CUTE but clumsy...AND sooo casual in that checked CARDIN...
smelling of CLOVE and COUGHING that certain COUGH
AND acting sooo conceited AND sooo condescending I could
choke...The creep
Oh...How can you care?
I mean the concept is sooo chaotic...You know?
How CAN you care
for a conceited clown...with caps on his cuspids...
a CLAIROL curly coif...a less than CAMAY complexion
and chafed and chawed on cuticles...
WHO's on the cusp of CAPRICORN...on crutches...AND
constantly in a crowd? THE CREEP
He can chew chalk and cackle for all I care
AND in that connection and in conclusion
I'll call you CHAR CHAR and we'll have a CHAT CHAT
                To be continued
I'm going to clean the closet

Oh CHAR CHAR
I care
I care

CHARLES C. CLOSKEY
212 619...7146
CALL AFTER CHURCH

D

DAVID is a drag
A definite dragged out drag
And if you've definitely decided to ask me to the
December Derby Day D O DAVID...Don't...Don't DAVID Don't...
I don't want to go to the December Derby Day DO and that's def
I will definitely D-I-E-...Die
definitely D-E-D...DEAD ...if DAVID asks me...
I mean it's not def if DAVID's definitely dragging DONNA DANFORTH
OR if DONNA is dragging DICKY DUNFEE
OR if DAVID is definitely dragging DOTTIE DREW
OR if DOTTIE is definitely dragging DODIE DOBBS
I mean...It's not DEF...
Oh it's such a drag and so indefinite I could die it's so indefinite
If only DAVID had one dram of decency he'd be definitely DARRLING...
But down deep I've decided deep down DAVID's definitely droop dry
and that's D E F
Anyway
I've decided to wear my dingle dangle DIOR drag
and my dragged out diamond dragon DELMANS and that's D E F
Oh DAVID do drag yourself out of the darkroom and drive over on
your DUCATI 450 DESMO SPECIAL HEAD and let's DAAANNNCCCE...

Oh DAVID
You destroy me
and that's D E F

DAVID DRUMMOND DOOLEY
212 718...6570
DISCONNECTED?
DEFINITELY DEF

EGMONT is everything
EEEK!
Eleven P.M.
EGMONT not in...ENCORE...
too early encore
and
I am sitting in my earphones
in an electronic euphoria
eating an egg
enjoying English ERIC on EPIC on the earphones
reading Esquire
and thinking of EGMONT
EGMONT is earthy and exotic and ephemeral
and everything else
and has one eye that enjoys going East...
the extra one enjoys EUGENIA ENTWHISTLE
EEEEEEKY EEEEEK!
Anyway...
EGMONT is at ELAINE EVERSHARP's this evening
exercising his earth-shattering ego
and
ERIC is coming through encore
into my electronic euphoria
ERIC ERIC you're electric ecstasy
E R I C......E C S T A S Y!
I'll play you encore while I entertain
the electronic idea of telephoning
EGMONT
encore and encore and encore and encore

Oh EGMONT
I'm exhausted
and on top of
everything else
I have an EARACHE
EEEEEEEEEK...

EGMONT E. EDENS
212 804...3977
EXTENSION
EACH EVENING AT ELEVEN
or EVEN EARLIER OR LATER

F

FARNSWORTH is a fud
and
Frankly I fail to see the fascination
On Friday the FIFTH I had the FLU and a fever and felt foul...
so I filed over to FRIEDA's in a flurry of festive foo...for
FRIED FREAK AND FEY FOOD in my fogged up FRENCH focals and
fuchsia feather Boa...and
T H E R E was FARNSWORTH...in the fone booth...looking sooo
Fantastic I could faint he looked sooo Fantastic...
with that fantastic flaxen hair and fantastic floppy hat...and
those FAANNNTASSSTIC freckles...fingering his fringe...and
eating a FRENCH FRY...looking so FANTASSSTIC I could faint...
and he hung up the fone and filed out in a flurry of festive foo
to find FRANCINE FOTHERGILL...THAT frump...in front of FRIEDA's...
in full color...in FERRARI...FARROOOOOOM...
and he filed in the front seat...FAROOOOM...to fly to flick and
FILLMORE's to finish off Friday till four...
FAAARROOOOOOOOOM and FOO...
OH
FAREWELL FARNSWORTH and FORGET it...
FRANKLY I've forgotten every feeling I ever felt for you...
and
FRANKLY
FRANCINE is far from a friend and her hair is FRIZZ
and her freckles are FAKE and she's FAT FARNS...
FAT FAT and FICKLE...You Fool

Oh FARNSWORTH
Friend or FOO
You are
FANNNNTASSSSTIC

FARNSWORTH FAIRWEATHER
516 917...5808
FIX THE FONE FARNSWORTH
I'm F R A N T I C and
I keep getting the F B I

G

GIG is goo
Goooey in fact...but GOOD goo...You know?
and is soo good looking and soo GIG and soo GO
it grabs you right in the gring grong...You know?
But Gad...
I've GOT to get going...and
get over to that GRAFFITI GALLERY...above GRISTEDE'S...where
GIG goes to feed the goldfish...and...GLOM onto that guitar
and Oh GAD...
when GIG goes GRUMMMMMA GRUMMMMMMa GRUMMM on THAT guitar...
with that grin...and...that green gauze gaze...GOOO-EEEY...
It is soo gutsy and soo GIG and soo GOOOEY GROANY...and
GYPSY in fact...but GOOD gypsy...You know?
I've GOT to get going...
But Gad...
He COULD have GONE downstairs to GRISTEDE'S...for a geranium
or grass seed...or garlic...or GROUND ROUND...Goo...
Granted...GIG's gamey...but GOOD gamey...You know?
Anyway
I've GOT to get going and get a goo gift of goggles to give GIG
A N D
I've G O T to get to GREENWICH...GIG's going...GOOOOOEY...

Oh
GOOD GAD GIG
You're GORGEOUS

GIG G. GUGGI GROTE
212 706...2576...GARAGE
212 908...4289...GALLERY
212 407...3912...GRISTEDE'S
GIG's GEMINI...GOO
IS THAT NOT GOO?

HENLEY is hateful
I mean HENLEY is sooo hateful I could heave he's sooo hateful...
Oh HENLEY...I HATE you...AND your honey HALO hair...AND
your headband...
You're HORRID HENLEY and HARDLY a human...
AND as it happens HENLEY...that's only HALF...
I HAPPEN to have HEARD how you were hanging around on your
HARLEY CHOPPER 74...HAROOOM...AT HOOLIHAN's HARDWARE AND HINGES
AND how you HAPPENED to get in a HUDDLE with HEIDI HETTINGER
HO HO AND HO...AND HOW you HANDED her your HOROSCOPE...AND
she was HYSTERICAL...HO HO and HO
I mean
How HILARIOUS HENLEY...How HUMOROUS...HA HA and HO...
Well HARDLY!...Oh how could you HENLEY?
How COULD you be so HATEFUL?
Here's a hint HENLEY...
I have had it...so HUSH...I have a headache AND I'm in a hurry
AND I have to do my hair...AND I have to HEAVE...H E L P...

Oh Henley
Honey
I hate you
Why do you hate me?

HENLEY HOBLITZELLE
212 508...3304
HANG UP IF YOU HEAR
A HICCUP
H E L P

I

INNY is an idiot
The idiot
and for INNY to imagine that I am interested in INNY
is instant insanity...
I had no idea that INNY was interested in the idea that
I was interested in INNY
AND
IF I have insinuated...or given the impression that I
am interested in INNY...
It is instant imagination and illusion...The idiot
I mean
for INNY to infer that I have the itsiest inkling of an
interest in that irky individual...is inconceivable and
instant insult...AND I would rather incarcerate myself
indoors indefinitely...I AM...NOT INTERESTED...
Incidentally
Insofar as INNY is interested in insects...he likes
IVY INGERSOLL...that instant itch...
and
does these idiotic imitations of ISABEL IBBING that iceberg
(Indescribable)
In any case
INNY has I.I. inscribed on his insteps in INDIA INK...
(I.I.)?...I hate inscriptions...INSTANT INDULGENCE...
INNY is an idiot...I find him impossible...I LIKE him

Oh INNY
I am INFATUATED

INCE ISSHERWOOD
212 619...9831
IF INCOMMUNICADO
ASK
INFORMATION

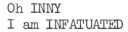

JOSH is a JERK
and
is
sooo jazzed up on JR. JOHANSEN...THAT jackass
that
JERKY JOSH does whatever JACKASS JR. does...The Jerk...
It's just such a JOKE...
Just last
January...JR. got this bottle green JAG...X K 120...and
got jazzed up on JACKIE JICKER-JOHNS...THAT JERK...
who has this gigantic JAZZ COLLECTION...The JACKASS...
Sooo JERKY JOSH got a bottle green JAG...X K 120...and
got jazzed up on JACKIE JICKER-JOHNS...The JERK...
THEN
Just last
JUNE...JR. jilted JACKIE JICKER-JOHNS and all that JAZZ
and
so did JOSH...the Jerk...JEEPERS...
Oh it's ALL sooo JUVE...
and
such a jazzed up JUMBLE...You know?
I mean
I like JR. the JACKASS
and
I like JOSH the JERK
BUT
since
JR. is January
and
JOSH is JUNE...AND...JUPITER's on the rise...
it J U S T proves
THAT
JR.'s a jazzed up JINX and a JACKASS and a JERK...JEEPERS...
I'm going to jazz myself off to JAMAICA on a JET...and
JUST vegetate...IT'S ALL JUST too JAZZY...You know?

Oh JOSH
I'm jealous of JR.

JOSH J. JASPER
201 718...2681
JUST IN CASE
201 804...0716
J. JOHANSEN JR.

K

KEVIN is kind of heaven
and
I keep KALEIDOSCOPING in on him

IT'S
A
KIND OF KEYHOLE KINESCOPE
ALL
KOHL AND KODACHROME
OF
A
KIND OF KOOKY KING
WITH
KIND OF KLIEGLIGHT KING'S CROSS EYES...

KIND OF KLINKING HIS KASITAR
ON
THOSE
KING KAKNOCKED KAKNEES...
IN
A
KUNGSITE ENCRUSTED KASHMIR KAMASUTRA SILK KAMEEZ...

A
KIND OF KING SIZE KING KONG CLOWN
IN
THOSE
KOOKY KHAKI KEDS...

Oh, KEV...I'm kinky for KABUKI
B U T...
You've G O T to be KIDDING
I keep KALEIDOSCOPING in on those KLIEGLIGHT KING'S CROSS EYES...

Oh KEVIN
KISS ME
KIIIIISSSSSS me

KEVIN K. KOCH
516 917...2391
KEEEEEEP at it...

LORENZO is lovable
not a lot
But I love the look of him
It's all Latin Lizard Louse
coming to you live in living
language like lightning down
lovely LEXINGTON AVENUE with
that long lemon lush LOVING CARE
hair flying...and his limpid
loud lizard LAPIS LAZULI eyes
leaping on the love of his life
his luminous lavender LAMBRETTA
with loads and lots of lunar
linear lear lustra luxe lights
Don't you love it?
He lives like a Lord
in that lackluster loner lower loft
in lounge leathered luxury
and lizard leathered LEVIS
with lovable lifts in his loafers
lapping a lager, and leafing
through Lawrence's Lady Chatterly's
Lover and leaving his lovable
laundry in another lower loft
in the lucky lap of that lovely
lilac luminary from LONDON
LAURIE LEHMAN...Don't you love it?

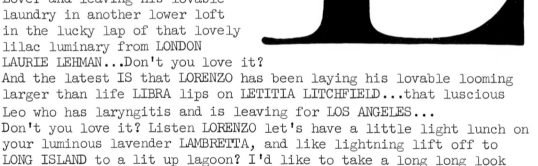

And the latest IS that LORENZO has been laying his lovable looming
larger than life LIBRA lips on LETITIA LITCHFIELD...that luscious
Leo who has laryngitis and is leaving for LOS ANGELES...
Don't you love it? Listen LORENZO let's have a little light lunch on
your luminous lavender LAMBRETTA, and like lightning lift off to
LONG ISLAND to a lit up lagoon? I'd like to take a long long look
at your looming larger than life LIBRA lips...LOVE

Oh LORENZO
LOOOOK at ME...
I LOVVVVVE you a LOTTTTT
How much laundry
is there LORENZO?

LORENZO LUIGI LOMBARDI
415 706...4406
LONG DISTANCE

MOO IS MAD
AND OUT OF HIS MIND FOR MOVIES
MINI MOVIE OF MOO BEING MAD FOR MOVIES
MONDAY...MAY...MIDMORNING
MOO MOVING DOWN MADISON IN MAUVE MUFFLER AND
MANGY MOROCCAN MOCCASINS MUNCHING MANGOES
MOVES RIGHT ON 53RD TO MODERN MUSEUM
MOVES THROUGH MAIN LOBBY AND MASSES OF MATISSES T O
MOVIE THEATRE ON MEZZANINE
REMOVES MANGY MOROCCAN MOCCASINS...LIGHTS OUT
MOVIE COMES ON

MARIA MONTEZ

AND THERE'S MARIA ON THE MESA
MEDIUM SHOT OF MARIA MOVING MOUTH
MEDIUM SHOT OF MOO MOVING MOUTH
MEDIUM SHOT OF MARIA MOANING
MEDIUM SHOT OF MOO MOONING
MEDIUM SHOT OF MARIA MUNCHING MANTILLA
MEDIUM SHOT OF MOO MUNCHING MANGOES AND MAUVE MUFFLER
MOVIE OVER...MUSIC UP...LIGHTS UP
INTERMISH
MOO MOTIONLESS...LIGHTS OUT
MOVIE COMES ON

MARIA MONTEZ

MOVIE OVER...MUSIC UP...LIGHTS UP
INTERMISH   MOO MOTIONLESS
MONDAY...MAY...MIDNIGHT
MOO MOVES TO PUT ON MANGY MOROCCAN MOCCASINS
MOVING MANGLED MANGOES TO FLOOR...
MOO MOVES FROM MEZZANINE...T O
MAIN LOBBY AND MASSES OF MATISSES
EXTERIOR MUSEUM...MOONLIGHT...CUT TO LONG SHOT
MOO MOVING UP MADISON MOONING ABOUT MARIA
DISSOLVE...CUT...PRINT...
MOO MOO THE MOON IS MOO...FADE OUT
MEANWHILE BACK AT THE MARKET PLACE...

OH MOO
I'M MUCHO MAD
FOR YOU MOO
AND I MEAN MUCHO

MOO M. MUMSFORD
212 407...8802
NEVER ON MONDAY
MOO IS A MUST
NOT TO BE MISSED

NEDDY is nauseous
and
never will be anything BUT nauseous...The Nit
Neat...Nifty...Natty...Nauseous NEDDY...
I mean the NERVE of NEDDY...nipping off to NEWPORT on
New Year's Eve...NAROOOM...on that NORTON COMMANDO...
NAROOOM...for NEPTUNE's and NYMPHS' NIGHT...NAROOOM...
without so much as a nod...NAROOOM... and staying until
the 19th...NAROOOM...
Is that not the nauseous Nth degree of nothing and NAROOOM?
and
the next thing you know...NEDDY is back...
Nipping around New York...and we're having
NEDDY NOSE IN THE AIR WEEK...and the name of the game IS
WILL HIS HONORABLE NEDDY NIBS deign to NOD...or NOT?
So much for nausea...
NEEDLESS to note and to the naked eye
NEWPORT did NOTHING for NEDDY...You know?
I mean
It's the same old nearsighted NEDDY
with the same old nipped in nostrils
STILL nibbling the same old NEDDY nails
DOWN to the same old NEDDY nubs...
NOT that I've NOTICED...
I haven't been noticing NEDDY...NOT since NOVEMBER the 9th...
the night of the NECCO-NUCOA NUPTIALS...and I never will...
no matter what...NEWPORT or NO NEWPORT...You know?
What's there to NOTICE?
NEDDY does do nice needlepoint...
NOT that I'VE noticed

Oh NEDDY
NOD to me
or I'LL NEVER
notice you again
For the love of NED
NEDDY...N O D

NEDDY NEIDERLANDER
516 908...9209
NEW NUMBER
NOW or N E V E R
NINE ON THE NOSE AT NIGHT
NOON ON THE NOSE
      OR
NIP OVER TO NEDICK'S

O.O. is older
not OLD older...but ooogey older...You know?
and I had this OOOGEY opportunity of giving O.O. the O.O.
at the opening of OTHELLO...at that OPERA BAR which was
soo overcrowded with all those opera oriented outcasts...
and he was ONLY overwhelming...in his orchid velvet and
all of those ooodles of opals...with his oboe in his pocket...
looking soo overwhelmingly ooogey...and soo obviously older
I could ooops...
I mean
with those ocelot orbs soo oblivious to the outside world...
and that O.O. mouth saying OOOOO...and ordering an orange over...
Oh OOOGEY...I mean OOOGEY OGG...
I mean
O.O. is ONLY out and out overpoweringly overwhelming...
OBESE...but...overwhelming...You know?
Of course...there could be this ONE obstacle...
I mean
O.O. DOES have this sort of overhanging occlusion...
I mean...His TEETH DO stick OUT...
which could be this ONE obstacle...and I've thought about it...
OFTEN...Oh...if only...
BUT...offhand...
I mean the orchid velvet...and the opals...
and the oboe in the pocket...A N D the being OLDER...You know?
I mean the OVERALL is ONLY overwhelming...and...
I am openly and overpoweringly OVERWHELMED...OOOGEY...and
on top of that
He is OCTOBER...You know?

Oh O.O.
You're the 0 and 0
I think I'LL go
make an omelette

O.O. OAKES
203 917...4313
OUT OF ORDER?

PETER is POMPOUS
I
mean
He is so pompous I could perish he's so pompous
PETER's passion is PETER and
He is possessed
with this purple portfolio
of
PICTURES of PETER
PETER posing at a premiere
(with picture people)
PETER posing at plush posh pom pom party at the Plaza
(ears like propellers)
PETER plunging into POLLY POTREE's polluted pool
(feet like pontoons)
PETER posing in PETER's Porsche with POLLY's poodle PATRICK parked by pal
(eating a pizza with policeman and parking ticket)
PETER playing ping pong in POLLY POTREE's patio in pith helmet
(POLLY paddling PETER) (wearing python pants)
PETER the pin up...the prophet...the pain
PETER the plastic...the pasteurized priss
PETER the peer...the pure puree of popcorn
THE PRINCE AND THE POET AND THE PIGEONTOED POOP
OH PETER PLEASE   YOU POMPOUS PUFFED UP PEACOCK
PHOOEY

Oh Peter
You're PERF!

PETER PAYNE POTTER
212 508...3712
PLEASE PICK UP THE PHONE
PETER
P R O N T O

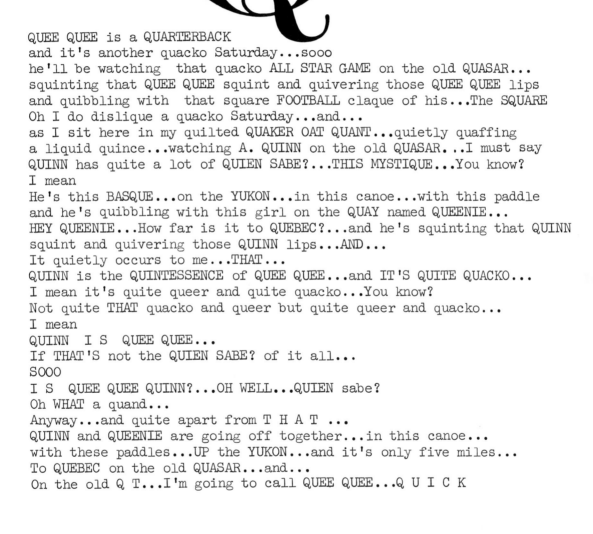

QUEE QUEE is a QUARTERBACK
and it's another quacko Saturday...sooo
he'll be watching that quacko ALL STAR GAME on the old QUASAR...
squinting that QUEE QUEE squint and quivering those QUEE QUEE lips
and quibbling with that square FOOTBALL claque of his...The SQUARE
Oh I do dislique a quacko Saturday...and...
as I sit here in my quilted QUAKER OAT QUANT...quietly quaffing
a liquid quince...watching A. QUINN on the old QUASAR...I must say
QUINN has quite a lot of QUIEN SABE?...THIS MYSTIQUE...You know?
I mean
He's this BASQUE...on the YUKON...in this canoe...with this paddle
and he's quibbling with this girl on the QUAY named QUEENIE...
HEY QUEENIE...How far is it to QUEBEC?...and he's squinting that QUINN
squint and quivering those QUINN lips...AND...
It quietly occurs to me...THAT...
QUINN is the QUINTESSENCE of QUEE QUEE...and IT'S QUITE QUACKO...
I mean it's quite queer and quite quacko...You know?
Not quite THAT quacko and queer but quite queer and quacko...
I mean
QUINN I S QUEE QUEE...
If THAT'S not the QUIEN SABE? of it all...
SOOO
I S QUEE QUEE QUINN?...OH WELL...QUIEN sabe?
Oh WHAT a quand...
Anyway...and quite apart from T H A T ...
QUINN and QUEENIE are going off together...in this canoe...
with these paddles...UP the YUKON...and it's only five miles...
To QUEBEC on the old QUASAR...and...
On the old Q T...I'm going to call QUEE QUEE...Q U I C K

Oh QUEE QUEE
I'VE GOT to
QUIET DOWN
I feel queasy

060

QUEE QUEE LUIS QUINTEROS
819 619...6798
ONE QUESTION QUEE QUEE...
WHAT'S THE SCORE?

R

```
RODNEY is RODNEY
I mean...
REALLY
Are you ready for RODNEY?
red headed rat...
RIGHT...
rank and raucous?...
RIGHT...
reckless?...
RIGHT...
ridiculous?...
RIGHT...
repulsive?...
RIGHT...
riddles his records?...
RIGHT...
rude to his radio?...
RIGHT...
rash with his raincoat?...
RIGHT...
reeks of rag rubbish?...
RIGHT...
can't remember?...
RIGHT...
doesn't want to remember?...
RIGHT...
runs after Rita Rothermore?...
RIGHT...
runs right away to Ruthie Reethemere?...
RIGHT...
reads in the rain?...
RIGHT...
ROTTEN?...
RIGHT!...
RODNEY is really ROTTEN
If you're ready
```

Oh Rodney
I'm ready

```
RODNEY RUTHERFORD
212 407...4491
LET IT RRRIIINNNGGG!!!
REACH FOR THE RECEIVER,
ROD...you rat
```

S

STEPHEN is something
and
Oh STEPHEN
I saw you at the SOUTH STATION on Sunday...looking soo simply
smashing in your sideburns and silver SUN and SKI shades...
and snow leopard...sliding off of your shiny silver scooter...
staggering under six satchels...six sacks of Sea and Ski...
stacks of skis...your shrieking STEREO...Steppenwolf and your
sleeping bag and that slob SHARON STUTTGARDT...SHRIEK...
HOW can you stand those Sagittarius saddle shoes STEPHEN?...and
standing in line for sleeping car space to SUN VALLEY...and I said
to myself...Sooo STEPHEN'S on the SPECIAL SKI SECTION of the seven
o'clock to SUN VALLEY...for snow...
Sooo
Since I had been standing there since six...in my skin tight
saffron sweater and SWEDISH suede skirt...studying SEGOVIA...
I saw you STEPHEN and I was sooo startled and sooo stunned and
SOOO surprised...and I started to speak...but you suddenly
looked sooo sheer smiling shark...and sooo sheer stupid SAP...
and sooo sheer super star...you didn't see me...SHRIEK...
Sooo STEPHEN
If you don't choose to speak to me...SAY SO...
In short...Speak up or shut up...
SHUT up STEPHEN...SHHHUUUUTT UP...You're sickening stuff...
SHRIEK...
Stay still a sec STEVE...
My salami sandwich is stuck to the sole of my shoe...SHRIEK...

Oh STEPHEN
You're sooo
SEXY
Are you SCORPIO?

STEPHEN SONNABEND
212 508...9436
Switchboard
Ask Stephen if he
received the
SWISS CHOCOLATE sent
on the sixteenth
from GSTAAD

TITI is Tedious
and
I am truly TIRED of TITI talking on the telephone...
I have tried three thousand times tonight to get through
to TITI to tell him that he TALKS too much...AND...if I
ever DO...I'm going to tell him that I am truly ticked off
AND tired of it...
I mean
To tell it TRUE...I'm tired of TITI...You know?
He's
Too tall and TOO thin and TOO terribly tight trenchcoat
TOO thoroughly tigertooth and TOO totally turtleneck...
He's
TOO tennis on Thursdays
in
THAT TOO tacky T shirt
TOO thoroughly TROPHY and TOO totally tournament...
AND
to top THAT
TITI took a TOTE BAG of TAPES and that trashy TOOTIE TUXTON
whose toe was in TRACTION...to TEANECK on THANKSGIVING...
in that TRIUMPH with the Top down...and TITI taped TOOTIE
TRILLING TRAVIATA...trash...and then TOOTIE taped TITI...
talking tiresome TURKEY talk in that TERRIBLE twingy twang
of TITI's...
Oh...It's all sooo tonsillitis...and to tell it true...
TITI's totally TAURUS...and his thighs are TOO thick...AND
He's truly a TROUT...
I think I'll throw up

Oh TITI
You're TRULY TOTAL
I'll be in touch

T.T. THORNTON
214 706...6752
TOLL CALL
TRY TUESDAYS
TRY TOMORROW
TRY TONIGHT

U

ULYSSES is unreal
and
that is the understatement of the Un universe
I mean he is so UN he's ugh and so UGH he's UN
UNreal UNcouth UNclean UNconscious and uncommonly UNcola
I mean he's utterly UGH and I like him...
I mean I have this utterly unreal and urgent urge for ULYSSES
and to my undying day I will never understand it...You know?
Everything about him is UGH...He's this urchin type...
utterly underweight...with this underslung jaw...and this
underbrushish hair...with this head underneath...and numero UNO
among his UNassets is this unreal uncle UMBERTO...UGH...
who plays the UKE...if you can bear the ugh of THAT...
OH
It is so unreal and so utterly ugh...I could urgle it's so
unreal and so utterly ugh...BUT I like him...You know?
AND
the ultimate ugh of all the ughs IS...that ULYSSES has this
unreal and urgent urge for URSULA UBBERSTADT...UGH UGH and UGH...
and to my undying day I will never understand THAT...
Oh what's the use?
Anyway
I understand by the underground that ULYSSES has an UN ULCER...
How UN UTOPIA...
Oh UGH...It's all so UN...I utterly do not know...You know?

Oh ULYSS
You undo me
and will until
my undying day

ULYSSES UARKOS
801 908...4192
UNLISTED
URGENT
UGH

VAL is V V (Very Vanilla)
All veins and vest (Very VICUÑA) and VERY Velour hat out
A Visual Art with these VOLLEY ball eyes and this
V V V (VERY VACANT VANILLA) stare...and V V V I P ...with
ALL of this savoir faire...You know?
I mean
He is just sooo voulez vous I could vomit...
and will if he ever says it again...
VAL is a VEG and is as VAGUE as...and on the verge of VIRGO
and lives in a V V void somewhere in the VILLAGE...
with VENETIAN blinds...VUITTON luggage and no ventilation
It's all V V V (VERY VIVID VANILLA)...You know?
BUT I do love that VEST...I mean it is VEREEE voulez vous...
Anyway
I'm going to put on my V neck voile
and rev up my VESPA (VEREEE VIOLETTE) and voulez vous over
to see if VAL has parked his V V (VERMILION VOLKSWAGEN)
in that vacant violation spot in front of LE DRUG STORE...
in back of VOGUE
ALL of a sudden I have this violent craving for a MILKSHAKE

Oh VAL
Oh VAL
I'll take VANILLA
Que VOULEZ VOUS?

VALENTIN DE LA VILLE
212 718...6093
VISITING HOURS ONLY
C'est la V V ...OUI?

Willy is wild
and
Wednesday
was this WILD WESTERN WALLOW-IN at WOOTY WEMBLEY'S walkup
on top of WOOLWORTH'S on Wall Street...and IT WAS WILD...
I mean the whole wide world was there...WALLOWING...in all
of this COUNTRY And WESTERN WHANNNG...It was W I L D ...
and so was WILLY...who went as J. WAYNE...wafting around in
that wild WATUSI wig...WHANNNG...WILLY wisteria wild eyed...
and wagging that super wide angle...which he was never without
WHANNNG...and winking at all of those weirdos and waltzing
or whatever with whatever...WHANNNG...AND WHOOHEE it was WILD
and when WOOTY wheeled in those whacked up waiters with all
those whooshy and withered weenies...WILLY went WILD...and
wrote WAHOOTY WOOTY all over WOOTY's whitewashed walls...
WHANNNG...WHAT a WAHOO...WESTERNwise it was WILD...and
went on into the wee wees...WHANNNG...
OUTSIDE on Wall Street...It was wet and windy...weatherwise
and I watched WILLY walk up to the WALDORF for waffles...
and somewhere in between WOOLWORTH'S and Wall Street...
I lost my wrist watch...BUT...it was worth it...WILLY wise
OH Wonderful WORLD of WEDNESDAY
Oh WILLY
Why weren't you watching me when I was watching you?
or WERE you?...OH WILLY...WERE you?

Oh WILLY
YOU worm...
What's with the WEEKEND?
WHERE? WHEN?

WILLY WILDENSTEIN
202 804...7049
WHEN IT'S WORKING

YARM is younger
and
Oh, YARM, YOU're yum...YOU're yummy...I'm yingy for YOU, YARM...yum!
I'm yingy for your yummy yellow sweater, YARM...It's yum...And
yingy for your yellow yarn socks, YARM...yum...And yingy for
your yummy yellow hair, YARM...It's yum...And YOU're yum, YARM...
And yet..........
Yesterday you yoo-hooed at YOLANDA YARBOROUGH on her yammering yellow
YAMAHA and her yammering yellow scarf and all that YARDLEY, YARM.....

YEA............
It was a yellow yesterday....a yellow haze of yellow socks and hair
A yellowed YOO-HOO...yummied and yingied in the yellow YARDLEYED air
Oh, YARM...I'm yawning...
And if YOU gave me a yellow yacht, I'd yawn...YOU ying yong yo yo!

Oh Yarm
I yearn
for the
Yellow of You

YARMAN Y. YOUNG
212 917...2054
Here's
a
Yoo hoo to YOU
From YOURS
Y O O   H O O

ZOOZ is zizzy
and
Oh so RAZZLE and DAZZ...Oh...
I mean
He has this zizzy kind of zizz about him that gets you
all zizzed up...and those ZOOMAR eyes that zooom in on you
and...ZOOM ZOOOM...you're zapped out and zonked...AND...
I mean zapped...You know?
And ZOOZ LOOKS so RAZZLE and DAZZ...I mean he's as thin as...
and has this zany ZULU hair that zizzes...and he wears this
zinnia in his ear AND designs all his own clothes like this
zonky ZEBRA shirt...zipped down to here...Oh ZOOZ...and this
zany ZIRCON the size of a ZEPPELIN around that neck...Oh ZOOZ
I mean it's all sheer RAZZLE and DAZZ... You know?
Anyway
ZOOZ is always alone and goes about his biz on that ZUNDAPP
bike...and he ZOOOOOOMS out into the ozone and gets zapped
out on ZEN in the azure...and I mean ZAPPED...OH ZOOZ!
ZODIAC wise...I don't know WHERE ZOOZ is...
PISCES?...ARIES?...
I mean
ZEUS?...ZANZIBAR?...ZURICH?

Oh ZOOZ
Wherever you is
ZOOM on in
And
LEZZGO

Z. ZACHARY ZANZU
516 706...5198
THE ZOO
I presume

is
the
unknown
boy
I
will
meet
tomorrow
and
if
he
notices
me
I
will
send
him
a
letter
and
sign
it
with
an
X
from

Miss Becky Beckingham